1 2 3 4 5

Jenny Ackland

At Home With NUMBERS

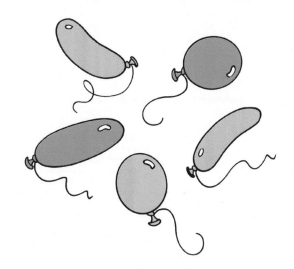

OXFORD
UNIVERSITY PRESS

1 2 3 4 5 1 2

Introduction

The *At Home With* workbooks introduce and reinforce key numeracy and literacy concepts for primary school children. They provide lots of opportunities to develop the key skills that are the basis of primary school curriculum work. The workbooks are available in three levels: 3–5 years, 5–7 years, and 7–9 years. The activities are fun and are designed to stimulate discussion, as well as practical skills. Some children will be able to complete the activities alone, after initial discussion; others may benefit from adult support throughout. All children will enjoy rewarding themselves with a sticker when they reach the end of an activity.

Using the book

At Home With Numbers offers a variety of activities which focus, in particular, on the following skills:

- hand–eye coordination

- recognition, understanding and writing of numbers 1 to 5

- counting and sequencing up to 5

- identifying sets of particular quantities

- understanding the terms 'more' and 'less'

- basic addition and subtraction.

Oxford University Press
Great Clarendon Street, Oxford OX2 6DP

Oxford University Press is a department of the University of Oxford.
It furthers the University's objective of excellence in research, scholarship, and education by publishing worldwide in
Oxford New York Auckland Cape Town Dar es Salaam Hong Kong Karachi
Kuala Lumpur Madrid Melbourne Mexico City Nairobi New Delhi
Shanghai Taipei Toronto

With offices in
Argentina Austria Brazil Chile Czech Republic France Greece Guatemala
Hungary Italy Japan Poland Portugal Singapore South Korea Switzerland
Thailand Turkey Ukraine Vietnam

Oxford is a registered trade mark of © Oxford University Press
in the UK and in certain other countries

© Jenny Ackland 2005
The moral rights of the author have been asserted
Database right Oxford University Press (maker)
First published 2005
Reissued 2009
This edition 2012

British Library Cataloguing in Publication Data
Data available

ISBN: 978 0 19 273325 2

5 7 9 10 8 6 4

Designed by Red Face Design
Illustrations by Mark Brierley, Oxford Illustrators
Printed in China

Paper used in the production of this book is a natural, recyclable product made from wood grown in sustainable forests. The manufacturing process conforms to the environmental regulations of the country of origin

Contents

☐ Number 1 4

☐ Recognizing 1 5

☐ Number 2 6

☐ Recognizing 2 7

☐ Sets of 1 8

☐ Sets of 2 9

☐ Sets of 1 and 2 10

☐ Counting 1 or 2 11

☐ Number 3 12

☐ Sets of 3 13

☐ Counting 1,2, 3 14

☐ Counting 1,2, 3 15

☐ Number 4 16

☐ Sets of 4 17

☐ Using 3 and 4 18

☐ Counting 1, 2, 3, 4 19

☐ Number 5 20

☐ Sets of 5 21

☐ Counting 1, 2, 3, 4, 5 22

☐ Counting 1, 2, 3, 4, 5 23

☐ How many? 24

☐ How many? 25

☐ More or less? 26

☐ More or less? 27

☐ Adding 1 28

☐ Adding 2 29

☐ Take 1 away 30

☐ Take 2 away 31

☐ Summary of skills 32

Number 1

Write number 1.

Give each dog 1 spot.

Give each cat 1 spot.

Recognizing 1

Colour 1 balloon.

Colour 1 flower.

Number 2

Write number 2.

Give each ladybird 2 spots.
Colour the ladybirds.

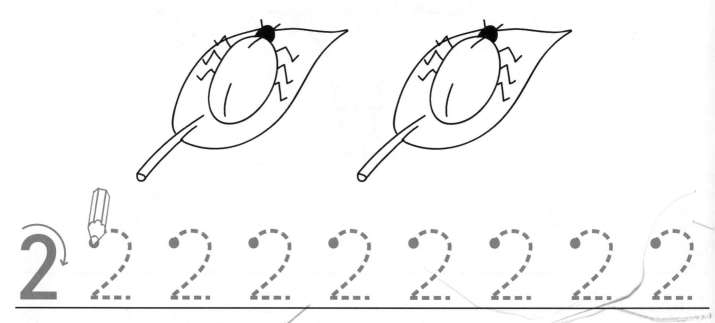

Give each butterfly 2 spots.
Colour the butterflies.

Recognizing 2

Colour 2 fish.

Colour 2 cars.

Sets of 1

Ring the trees with 1 apple.

Sets of 2

Ring and colour the sets of 2.

Sets of 1 and 2

Ring and colour the sets of 1.
Join them to the number 1.

Ring and colour the sets of 2.
Join them to the number 2.

Counting 1 or 2

Write over the numbers.

Count 1 or 2.

Number 3

Write number 3.

Give the balloon 3 spots.
Colour 3 trees.

Sets of 3

Ring and colour the sets of 3.

Counting 1, 2, 3

Write over the numbers.

How many?

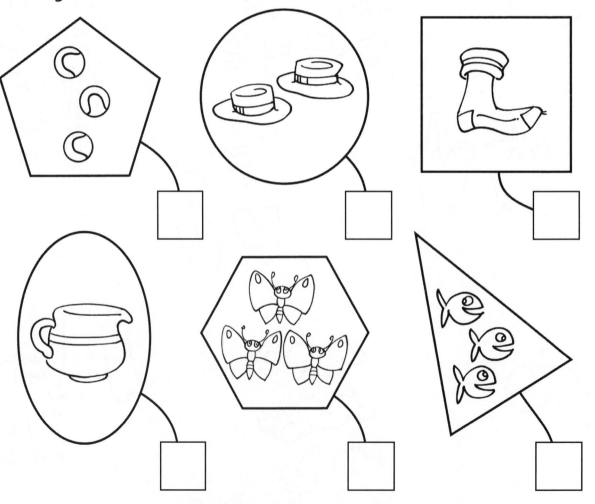

Counting 1, 2, 3

Write over the numbers.

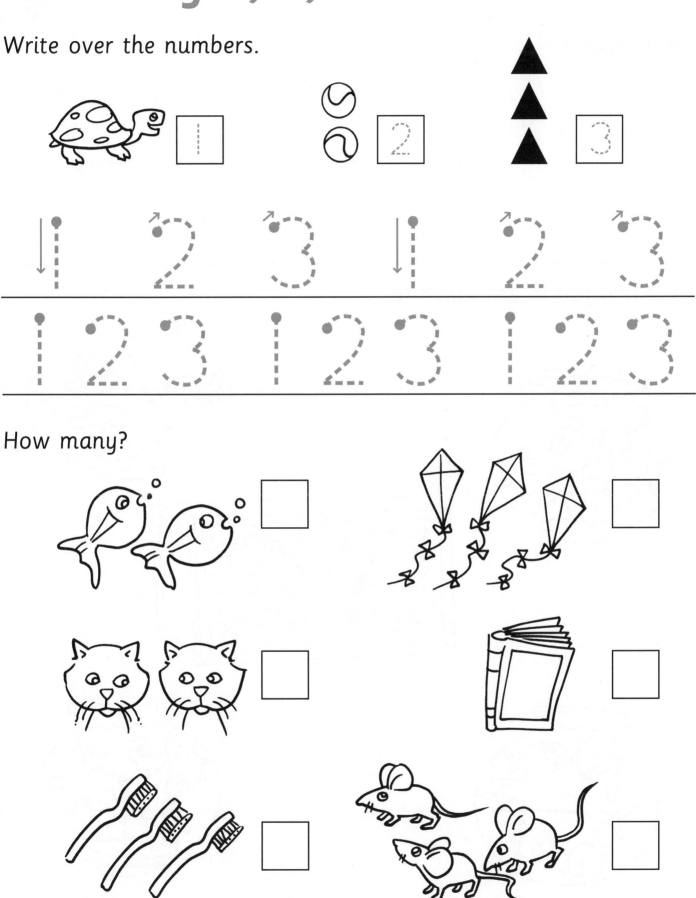

How many?

Number 4

Write number 4.

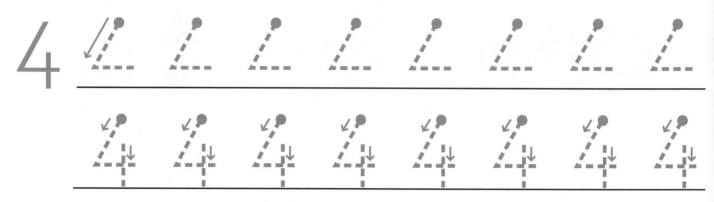

Colour 4 fish in each picture.

Sets of 4

Ring and colour the sets of 4.

Using 3 and 4

Read the numbers, then give the bugs 3 or 4 spots.

Counting 1, 2, 3, 4

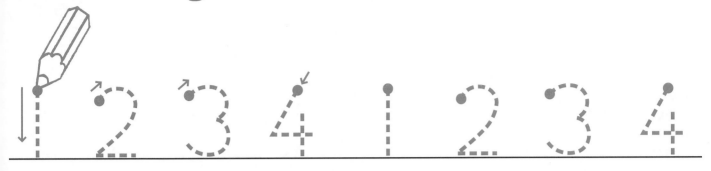

Count the pictures, then colour them.

Number 5

5 5 5 5 5 5 5 5 5 5

5 5 5 5 5 5 5 5 5 5

Colour 5 hats.

Sets of 5

Ring and colour the sets of 5.

Counting 1, 2, 3, 4, 5

1 2 3 4 5

Colour the pictures.

1 fish

2 rabbits

3 flowers

4 balls

5 trees

Counting 1, 2, 3, 4, 5

Count the pictures and circle the number.

 1 2 3 4 5 boot

 1 2 3 4 5 fish

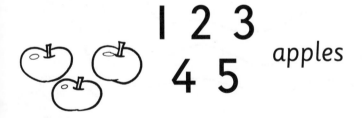 1 2 3 4 5 flowers

1 2 3 4 5 balloon

 1 2 3 4 5 apples

 1 2 3 4 5 house

 1 2 3 4 5 rabbits

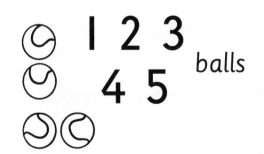 1 2 3 4 5 balls

How many?

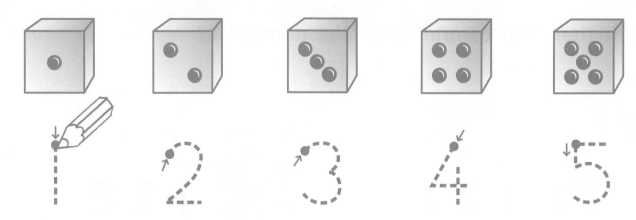

Give the snakes their spots.

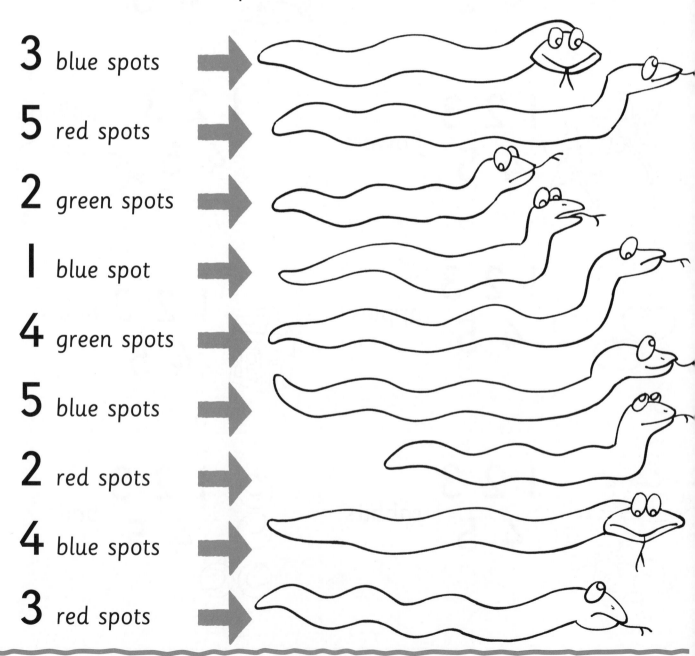

3 blue spots

5 red spots

2 green spots

1 blue spot

4 green spots

5 blue spots

2 red spots

4 blue spots

3 red spots

How many?

How many spots?

More or less?

Which set has more fish? Ring and colour it.

More or less?

Which set has less hats? Ring and colour it.

Adding 1

0   1   2   3   4   5

Add 1 more spot to each animal.
Count the spots on each animal.

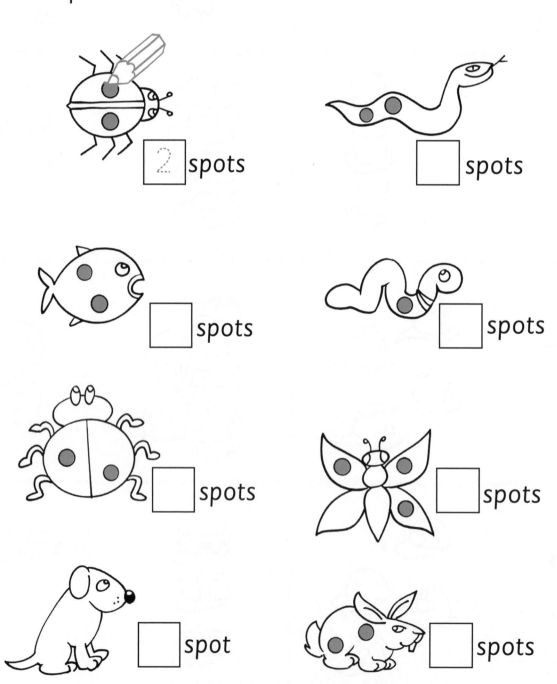

2 spots

spots

spots

spots

spots

spots

spot

spots

Adding 2

Add 2 more legs to each animal.
Count the legs on each animal.

Now there are [ ] legs.

Now there are [ ] legs.

Now there are [ ] legs.

Now there are [ ] legs.

Now there are [ ] legs.

Now there are [ ] legs.

Take 1 away

Take away the last number in each row.
How many are left?

Take 2 away

Take away the last 2 numbers in each row.
How many are left?

Summary of skills

Title	Page	Summary
Number 1	4	Writing and understanding the numeral 1
Recognizing 1	5	Recognizing the quantity of 1
Number 2	6	Writing and understanding the numeral 2
Recognizing 2	7	Recognizing the quantity of 2
Sets of 1	8	Recognizing a set of 1
Sets of 2	9	Recognizing a set of 2
Sets of 1 and 2	10	Distinguishing between sets of 1 and 2
Counting 1 or 2	11	Counting in sequence
Number 3	12	Writing and understanding the numeral 3
Sets of 3	13	Recognizing a set of 3
Counting 1,2, 3	14	Counting and labelling
Counting 1,2, 3	15	Counting and labelling
Number 4	16	Writing and understanding the numeral 4
Sets of 4	17	Recognizing a set of 4
Using 3 and 4	18	Drawing dots to correspond to numerals
Counting 1, 2, 3, 4	19	Counting in sequence and labelling
Number 5	20	Writing and understanding the numeral 5
Sets of 5	21	Recognizing a set of 5
Counting 1, 2, 3, 4, 5	22	Counting in sequence
Counting 1, 2, 3, 4, 5	23	Counting and numbering
How many?	24	Understanding numbers out of sequence
How many?	25	Understanding numbers out of sequence
More or less?	26	Introducing the concept of 'more'
More or less?	27	Introducing the concept of 'less'
Adding 1	28	Introducing addition
Adding 2	29	Introducing addition
Take 1 away	30	Introducing subtraction
Take 2 away	31	Introducing subtraction

At Home With 3–5 years		At Home With 5–7 years		At Home With 7–9 years	
abc	Reading	English	Phonics	English	Punctuation
Colours	Shape & Size	French	Spelling 1	French	Reasoning Skills – Verbal
Counting	Sounds & Rhymes	Handwriting 1	Spelling 2	Grammar	Reasoning Skills – Non Verbal
Letter Forms	Pattern & Shape	Handwriting 2	Times Tables	Maths	Spanish
Numbers	Writing	Maths		Mental Maths	